What Do Machines Do For Us?

Machines are very important. They help us to do our work more quickly.

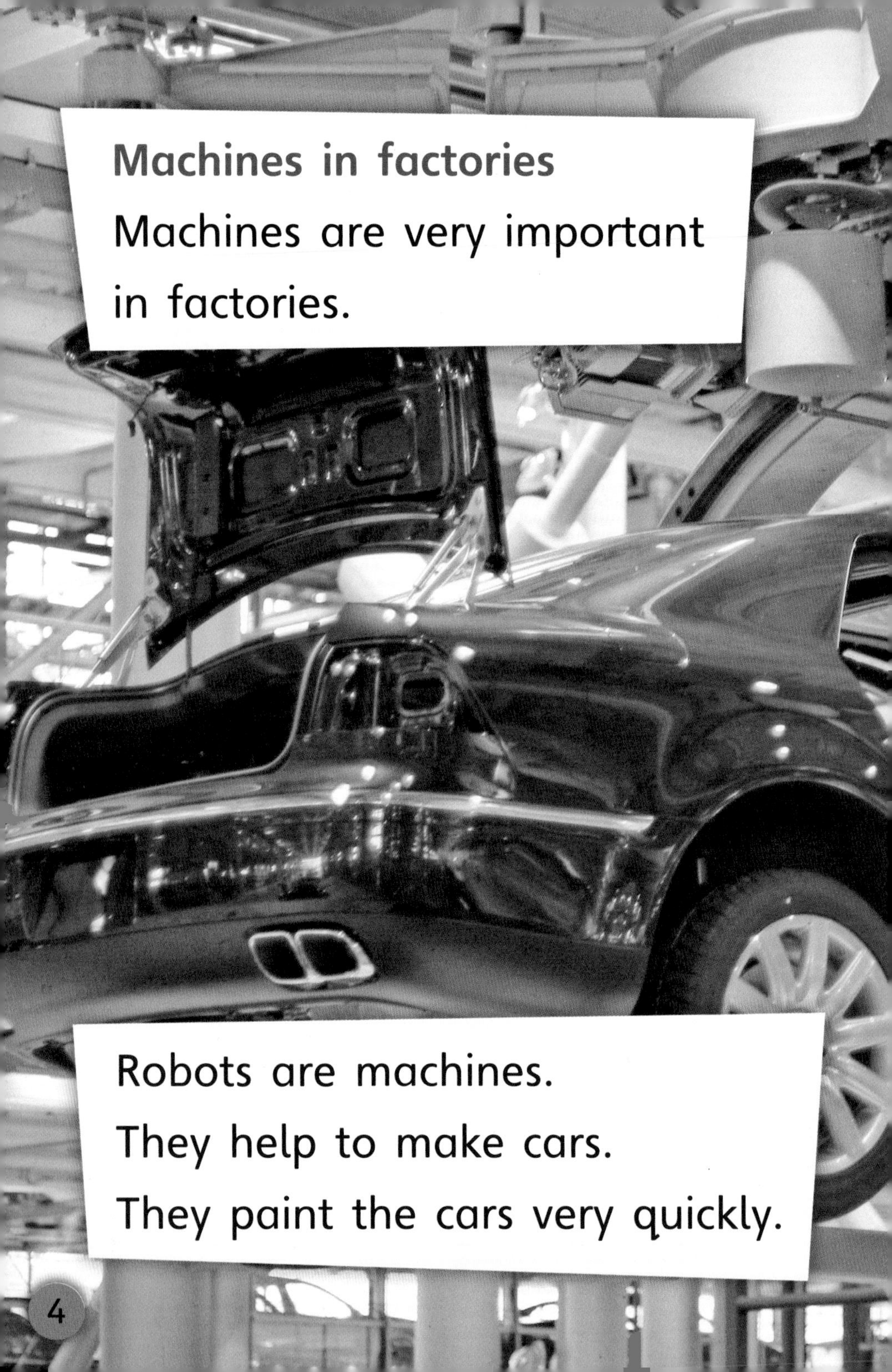

Machines in factories

Machines are very important in factories.

Robots are machines.
They help to make cars.
They paint the cars very quickly.

Contents

Simon Cheshire

Story illustrated by Chris Garbutt

Heinemann

Before Reading

Find out about

- Machines that help us

Tricky words

- machines
- important
- quickly
- factories
- building
- earth
- break
- careful

Text starter

Machines are very important. They help us to do our work more quickly. Big machines are used for building, and small machines are used by doctors.

Some robots are very big.
They help to move the cars in
the factory.

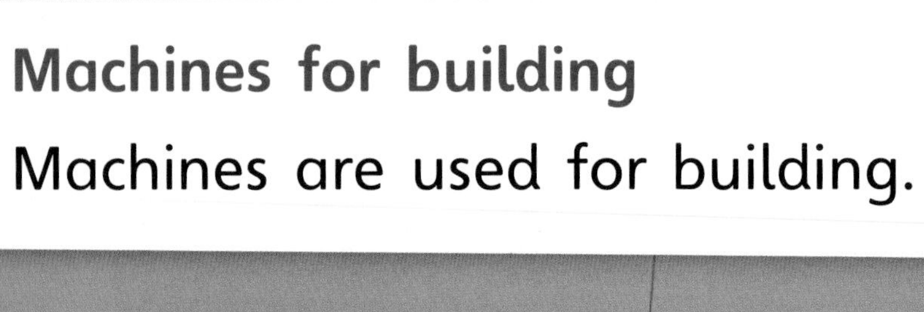

Machines for building

Machines are used for building.

These big machines help to build a house. They move the earth and stones for the builder.

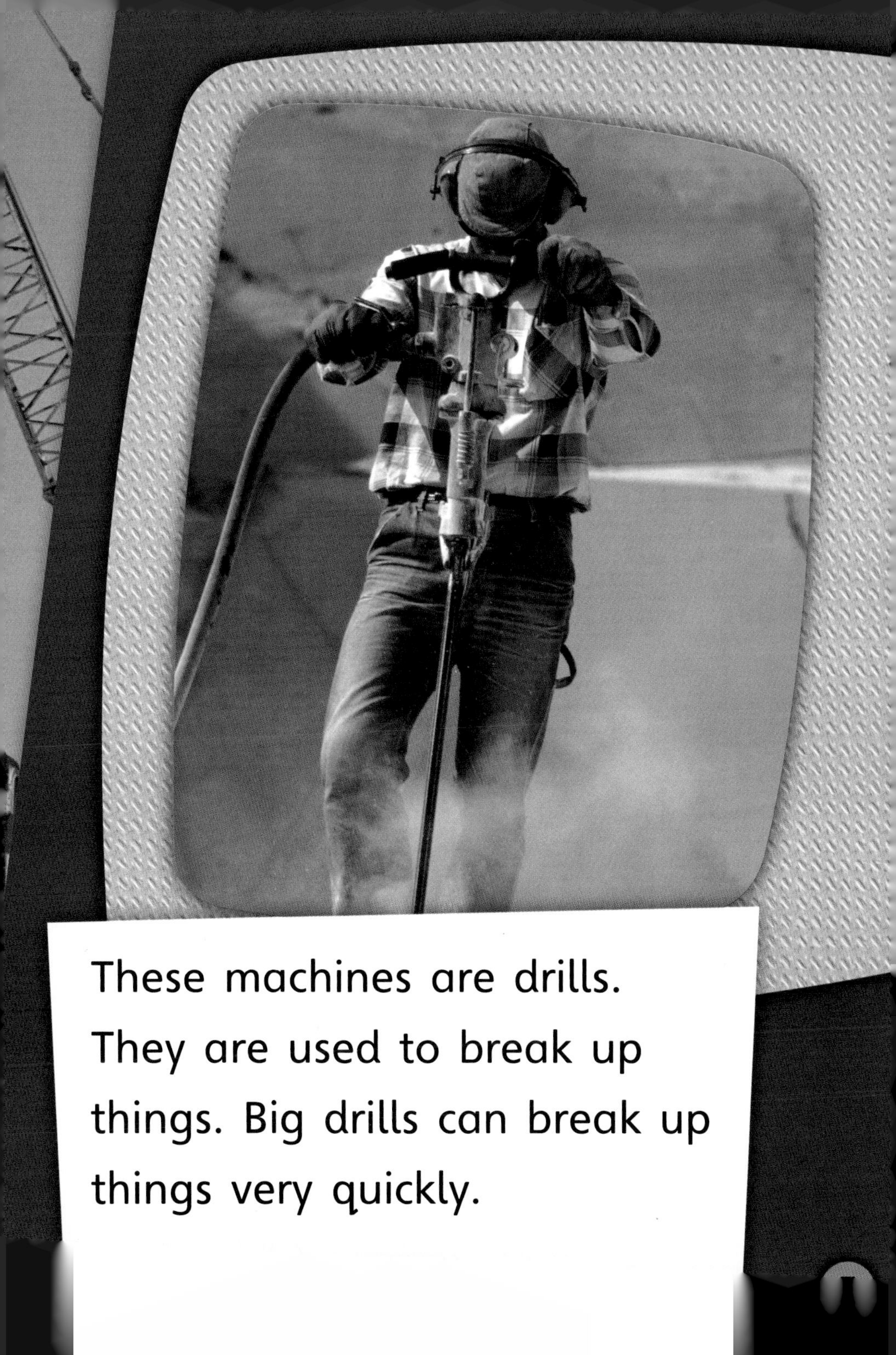

These machines are drills. They are used to break up things. Big drills can break up things very quickly.

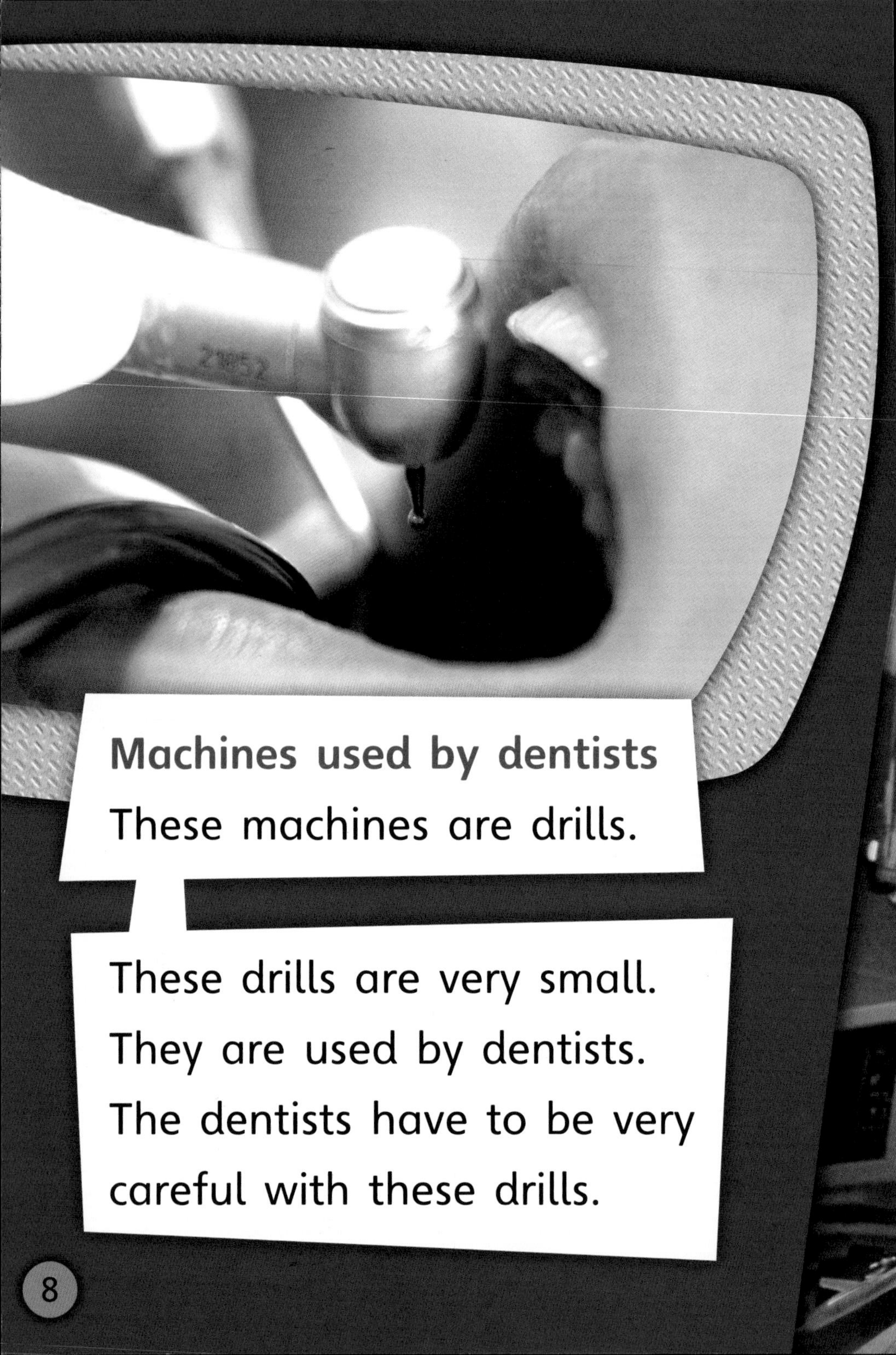

Machines used by dentists

These machines are drills.

These drills are very small.
They are used by dentists.
The dentists have to be very
careful with these drills.

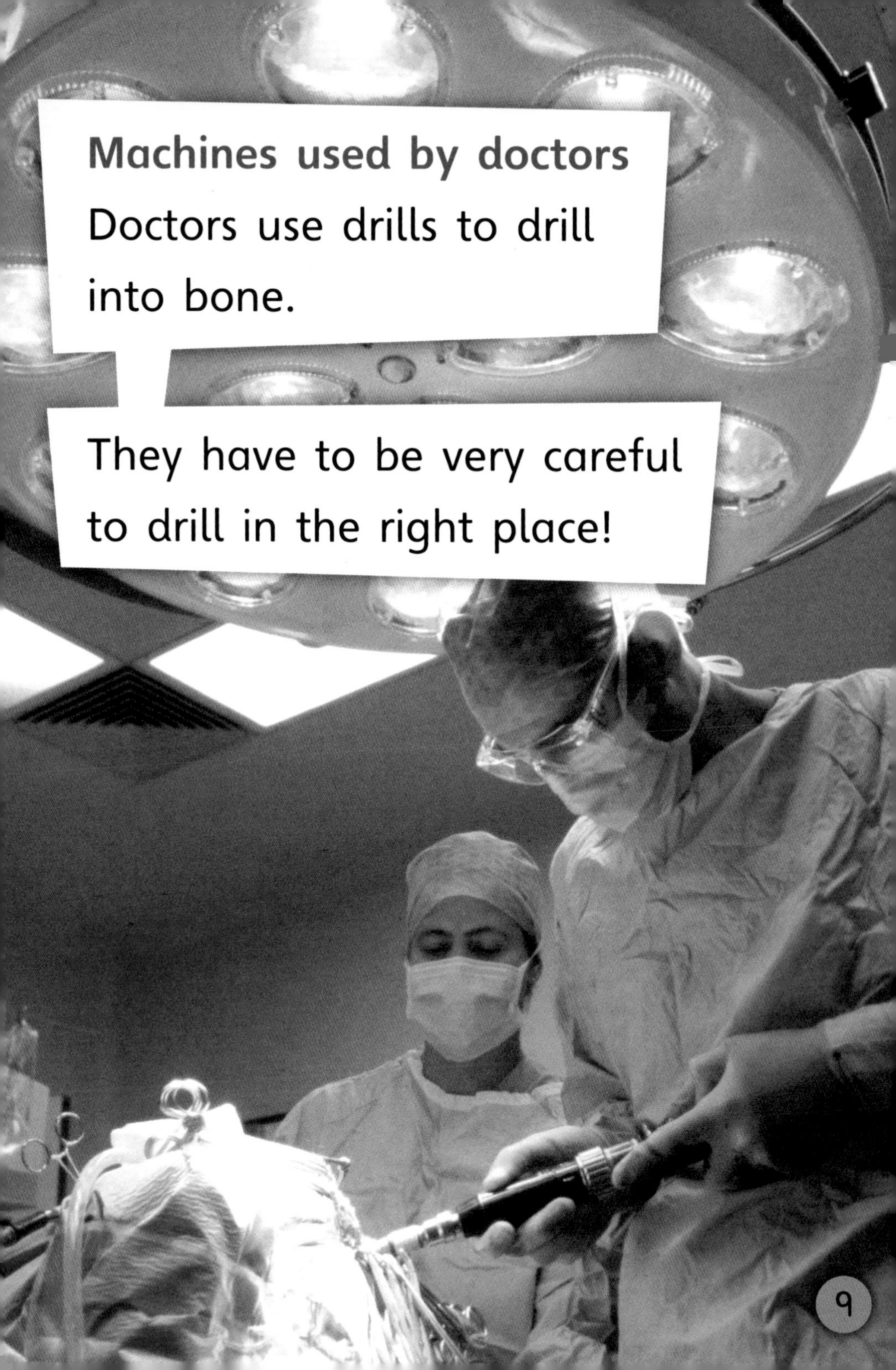

Machines used by doctors

Doctors use drills to drill into bone.

They have to be very careful to drill in the right place!

Machines are very important.
They help us to do our work.

What machines help you?

Quiz

Text Detective

- Why are machines important?
- What machines do you use?

Word Detective

- **Phonic Focus:** Initial consonant clusters

  Page 9: Sound out the four phonemes in 'drill'. Can you blend the first two sounds?
- Page 3: Can you find four words in 'important'?
- Page 9: Why is there an exclamation mark after 'right place'?

Super Speller

Read these words:

our more move

Now try to spell them!

HA! HA! HA!

Q What do you call a doctor with eight arms?

A A doctopuss!

Before Reading

In this story

Kirk, a Space Cop

Joe, a Space Cadet

Zorgon, their enemy

Tricky words

- Space Base
- Jet-Pack
- super-speed
- radar
- spaceship
- steal
- zoomed
- round

Story starter

Commander Kirk is a Space Cop travelling across Space in his starship. Joe, a Space Cadet, is on board too. Kirk and Joe battle against their evil enemy, Zorgon. Space Base has just sent Kirk their latest invention – a Jet-Pack that could go at super-speed!

Kirk and the Jet-Pack

Space Base gave Kirk a Jet-Pack.
The Jet-Pack could make Kirk
and Joe go at super-speed.

Joe looked at the radar.
"Sir," said Joe, "there is a spaceship on the radar."
Kirk looked at the radar.
"It is Zorgon," he said. "He is coming to steal the Jet-Pack."

"Sir," said Joe, "I have a plan. I will use the Jet-Pack to stop Zorgon."

Joe turned on the Jet-Pack.
But . . . he forgot to put the
Jet-Pack on.
The Jet-Pack zoomed off.

Kirk saw the Jet-Pack go.
"You have lost the Jet-Pack!"
said Kirk.
"Sorry, sir," said Joe.

Zorgon saw the Jet-Pack coming.
He jumped up to catch it.

But the Jet-Pack was going at super-speed and Zorgon couldn't stop it.

The Jet-Pack zoomed up and up
and round and round.

Zorgon zoomed up and up
and round and round!

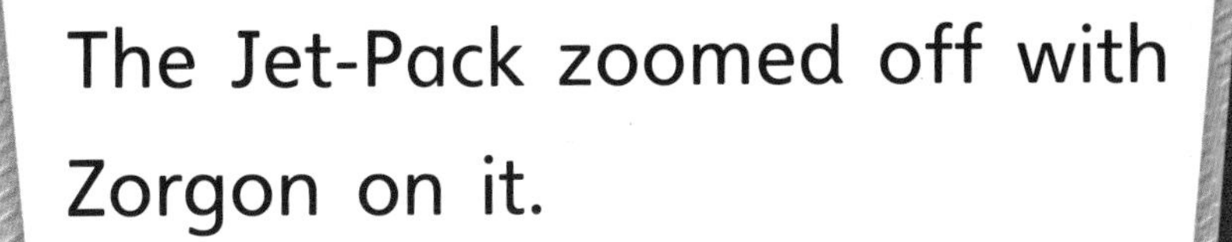

The Jet-Pack zoomed off with Zorgon on it.

“Just you wait,” said Zorgon. “I will be back!”

"Yippee!" said Joe. "I got rid of Zorgon!"

"Yes," said Kirk, "but you got rid of the Jet-Pack too!"

"Sorry, sir," said Joe.

Quiz

Text Detective

- What happened when Zorgon caught the Jet-Pack?
- Do you think Kirk will be cross with Joe?

Word Detective

- **Phonic Focus:** Initial consonant clusters

  Page 13: Sound out the four phonemes in 'speed'. Can you blend the first two sounds?
- Page 20: Can you find the word 'round' four times?
- Page 21: How many sentences are there on this page?

Super Speller

Read these words:

forgot catch round

Now try to spell them!

HA! HA! HA!

Q Can you telephone from a spaceship?

A Of course I can tell a phone from a spaceship!